Words
From The Brink
Stories and Poems
from Solstice Shorts Festival
2021
edited by
Cherry Potts

ARACHNE PRESS

First published in UK 2021 by Arachne Press Limited
100 Grierson Road, London SE23 1NX
www.arachnepress.com
© Arachne Press 2021
ISBNs
Print 978-1-913665-51-7
eBook 978-1-913665-52-4
Audio 978-1-913665-54-8
Library edition audio

Thanks to Muireann Grealy for her proofing.
Thanks to Komal Madar for her cover design.

Printed on wood-free paper in the UK by TJ Books, Padstow.

The publication of this book is supported using public
funding by the National Lottery through Arts Council
England.

Acknowledgements

After Before © Mandy Macdonald 2021

After This © Lucy Grace 2021

Apocalypse and *Now And Then* © Kate Foley 2021

Asteraceae © Lucy Ryan 2021

Because I Have Been Complacent About Climate Change © Angela Graham 2021

Betty Always Sees Herself From A Distance and *She Notices The Giant Grate Tilted* © Samn Stockwell 2021

Chronoflight © Tim Dillon 2021

Dominion © Robert René Galván 2021

Erosion © Jessica Conley 2021

Eunice Newton Foote, Gaia Theory and *When Describing Gaia* © Emily Ford 2021

Flood Warning and *Spring* © Xia Leon Sloane 2021

For Sale. One Planet. Well Worn. © Cath Holland 2021

Glacier, Calve Slowly © Corinna Schulenburg 2021

Humidity © Tara Willoughby 2021

Icarus and *Touch* © Karen Ankers 2021

Love Letter To The Earth © Jane Aldous 2021

Memory of Snow © Diana Powell 2021

Mr King Has Decided to Pursue Other Avenues © Rob Walton 2021

Mr McGregor's Seedlings and *PROFILE SERIES 832/1: Planet E¥338-ɸ* © Claire Booker 2021

Note To Self © Ness Owen 2021

Occupy Frogs © Lyndsey Weiner 2021

Potted Plants and *The Rain* © Jared Pearce 2021

Recharting The Territory © Stevie Krayer 2021

retablo for the deep ocean © Michelle Penn 2021

The Flooding © Rachael Li Ming Chong 2021

The Inescapable Irony Of Protective Packaging © Cathy Lennon 2021

The Last Lioness and *What The Natterjack Toad Teaches Us* © Kelly Davis 2021

Words
From The Brink

Contents

Introduction   8

Love Letter To The Earth   11

Potted Plants   12

Apocalypse   13

When Describing Gaia   14

Eunice Newton Foote   16

The Stars, Unfixed   18

The Last Lioness   22

Touch   23

Because I Have Been Complacent About Climate Change   24

Note To Self   25

Chronoflight   26

After This   28

These Days   30

Glacier, Calve Slowly   32

After Before   34

The Flooding   36

Mr King Has Decided to Pursue Other Avenues   38

Betty Always Sees Herself From A Distance   42

She Notices The Giant Grate Tilted   43

Views Of Greenland From Seat 39A   44

The White Boat   45

Erosion   46

Recharting The Territory   48

Memory Of Snow   50

Mr McGregor's Seedlings	56
Humidity	57
Yellow Brimstone	58
Weather For Politicians	59
This Rewilding Wind	60
Occupy Frogs	62
For Sale. One Planet. Well Worn.	63
Flood Warning	67
The Year Of The Tree	68
Now And Then	70
Dominion	72
What The Natterjack Toad Teaches Us	74
Asteraceae	75
retablo for the deep ocean	81
The Rain	82
We Are Beach People	84
The Inescapable Irony Of Protective Packaging	85
Spring	86
Icarus	87
Volunteer	88
This Is What You'll Get	93
The Undertaking	94
Gaia Theory	96
PROFILE SERIES 832/1: Planet E¥338-ɸ	97
The Things That Work	98

Introduction
Cherry Potts

This book is the seventh *Solstice Shorts* anthology, and represents the writing for the eighth Solstice Shorts Festival. All our festivals have a time theme, and generally are held at least in part, in Greenwich, on the Prime Meridian. This book may seem a little tenuous in its link, but the original call out was for *time is running out, a response to the climate crisis,* but that was a terrible title, and once the submissions started arriving, the new title, *Words From the Brink,* took form. Not so much catastrophising, as marginally hopeful – we can step back.

Words from the Brink is also the third in a series of anthologies loosely connected by the concept of Maps and Mapping; again, the link is circumstantial – where are we headed?

I was concerned that I would be inundated with end-of-the-world scenarios, and was haunted by a memory of a luridly illustrated double page spread in a (probably Marvel) comic that I read in primary school, which went something along the lines of *Some say the world will end in fire, Some say in ice.*

Cheerful stuff, and a strange way to be introduced to the poetry of Robert Frost!

Our versions seem to err towards drought or flood, but this is not a pessimistic book. It is filled with wonder and excitement and laughter (if often helpless and sardonic) at the glorious and vulnerable world we inhabit and her apparent capacity to thrive despite our depredations. But make no mistake, we know that seeming rejuvenation is false.

This book is a warning and, perhaps, a cry for help, from a *very* angry Gaia, who is prepared to take matters into her own hands, if we won't. It is also laced through with hope and signs of recovery, even in the post-apocalyptic scenarios envisioned by some writers.

More than one contributor thinks aliens could make a better job of caring for our planet, with a slightly despairing field report, and a brutal auctioning off of our very dubious assets. Seeds are sown deliberately and accidentally, children and animals treasured, signs of decay noted and fretted over, and escapes planned.

Here at Arachne we take our impact on the environment seriously, we know books aren't the greatest for the world in terms of power and water consumption, so we use wood free paper for our books, and recycled stationery and paper in the office, which is always used on both sides before being recycled again.

We use plastic free packaging, as do our printers, and we reuse every bit of packaging that comes into the building that is big enough to hold a book – so if your copy of this book arrived in bubble wrap, it has been round the block at least once already. Our electricity is already 100% renewable, and we are in the process of having solar panels fitted.

When our computers/phones give up the ghost we donate them to a local reuse and recycling charity. It is unquestionably not enough, so we urge you all

Do *SOMETHING*, while we still can.

Turn off that light, turn off that tap, turn down that heating; reduce, reuse, repurpose, recycle; plant a tree, protect the bees; write a song, a poem, a story that can reach the people who need to hear.

Shout about it. Protest!

Everything may yet be all right, but *only* with your help.

Jane Aldous
Love Letter To The Earth

Dear Old Bod,

ancient blue dot, wiser than the lot of us,
fragile as the most fragile, tough as old boots,

clods, we've trashed our own paradise,
turned nature on its head.

I can barely look at your smouldering lungs
and swollen arteries.

As every year turns, every solstice, every season,
I love you more fiercely, in all your raw, mucky,

translucent, charming magnificence. I want you to exist
until the sun burns you up and we all explode into stars.

All I have is my plot, where wild flowers run riotously
through crops.

And hope in the face of all hope that nature's beneficence
and human good sense will be enough.

Jared Pearce
Potted Plants

She's grown
the amaryllis so
tall it legs
across the counter,

trumpet bell
blossoms ringing
their glory
and devastation.

There's nowhere
to pull the stool,
swing over
and plop down,

and not get hit
by six blaring
hearts honking in my face
about the end

of times, valves
full or half or closing
closed, cup
mutes calling

the final turn
in our footsore
race, still miles
from a finish.

Kate Foley
Apocalypse

'Thanks to our viewer who sent
this wonderful sunset photo.'
The weatherman doesn't say
'taken at 6 am today'.

Whitehall says
'no panic' so
got up this morning,
scratched our armpits,
climbed in the shower,
kissed the kids,
time to go.

Used as we are
to 'climate change'
they call it,
and now the piercing frost
of stars at night
is hidden in the glare
of our inferior suns,

we never see the outraged universe,
just, but never kind,
thundering down the galaxies
to wipe us from its mind.

Emily Ford
When Describing Gaia

buxom is the first thing they say
 it is in their nature,
they are in hers:
the cirrus and nimbus surveying
 her great rolling quilt,
the way her long locks of hair
tumble
and
tumble into rapids
 in the West
  her rice staircases
   bulging into pregnant
       cherry blossom
          in the East
it is in her nature
she takes the dawn
in her arms
finds its heart with her lips
takes it between her teeth
   thrusting with her island hips
 here come those

entitled males
 those Titans, gods and men
 who will not find the heart in the sky
 who will not see her lips,
 or the teeth she bares,
 will not understand the whittled warnings
 of her tides
her sighing redwoods
 her screaming cracking plates
 they will plunder her flesh
 drill into her bones
she will give
              give
                 give
 everything they take
              take
          take

Emily Ford
Eunice Newton Foote

Dropping babies from our bodies like
                              mic drop
big as moons
relentless as light
these boons we bestow

so did you know
  Eunice (can I call her that?)
wrote: a*n atmosphere of carbonic acid gas*
would give to our earth a high temperature
in 1856
1856   1856   *1856*   *1856 1856*   *1856*
    1856   1856   1856   1856   1856
              1856   1856
                  1856   1856
                        1856
and after the obligatory
            SHUT UP, WOMAN
a man (I forget his name)
repeated her, and was applauded

hold onto your wombs ladies,
this is where it gets old
and tired
this happened again

and again
and again
and again
and while the planet is on fire,
we clap and we clap and we clap the men.

Elaina Weakliem
The Stars, Unfixed

The hissing of the water pump wakes me up in the middle of the night, and for a bleary moment, I grope through the sheets, trying to find the soft shape of your back. When the bed next to me turns up empty, I sit upright, panic clanging the primal alarm bells at the base of my skull.

I reach over to wake up your mother – and there you are, curled right up in her arms, your head resting on her collarbone. The two of you cling to each other unconsciously, your tiny hand pulling at the strap of her shirt. She rolls onto her back, bringing you up to her chest.

The water pump's hiss turns to a faint gurgle, and I scrub my hands across my eyes, falling back onto the mattress. The room hasn't started to show even the faintest signs of dawn, which makes me want to check the time, to see how long we really have left. The digital clock on the dresser is blank – the President made good on his promises and cut the power grid to most of our county yesterday. Only the water – what's left of it – is still running, thanks to the solar panels I installed to power the neighbouring irrigation systems, back when the threat of running dry loomed large, but unbelievable, on the distant horizon of the future.

Even on this last day, morning chores pull me out of bed and through the kitchen, grabbing the flashlight off the counter. The rituals are different from the ones I performed as a child, but since I turned thirteen, not a single morning has found me sleeping in after dawn.

It used to be cows that we raised out here – grazing

stock, mostly for beef. They were the first to go, seeing as they used the most water. The government was willing to subsidise our transition to an easier living, and the governor paid the bills while we tilled up the back pastures and seeded them with corn. Still, I'd be up at four, five o'clock, fixing the robotic harvesters, trying to memorise sections of your mother's programming books so she could sleep during the afternoons instead of sitting out in the shed, tinkering with the same malfunctioning thresher. She was tired all the time, and her doctor recommended bed rest. We knew from the beginning, Little One, that you'd be a force of nature.

Sometimes I wonder how I'll explain it all to you, how I can get you to understand words like 'subsidy' and how I'll find ways to make the history of this land relevant to you when it's not yours to keep anymore. I don't think they have cows in the Gulf colony. I think the scientists there have moved past animal meat.

The pump lets out a low wheeze, and I stoop down to check inside it with the flashlight's beam. Just as I thought, no clogs. The thing's just run dry.

Movement on the edge of the porch startles me, and I smack the flashlight into the pipes trying to stand upright. Your mother steps out into the beam of light, hands out in front of her in a silencing gesture. I offer her the flashlight, and she leans in to confirm the same thing as me. When she stands, she pulls me into her arms, the flashlight pressing into my back.

'You heard it too?' I rest my forehead against her neck. It's no cooler outside than it was in the bedroom, and we're both starting to sweat.

'Yeah.' She rocks from one foot to the other, swaying the two of us gently from side to side. 'I'm sorry, Isa.'

'It's not your fault.' I wonder again what time it is. How long we have left.

Little One, I know already that your mother will adjust fast to the colony. She's good with computers and kids, and her cousin's managed to get her a job in the settlement. She'll fit right in, make friends with our neighbours. She's not even discouraged by the lack of sunlight. She's been trying to get me interested in the logistics of plankton cultivation. I couldn't care less about deep-sea fish or whale food, but I haven't said that aloud. She's trying her best; both of us know that I belong up here.

'I guess that's the last of the groundwater,' I say, my mouth dry. 'I should go check to make sure we've got everything in the truck. We don't want to have to come back for any of it once we leave.'

'Hey.' She catches my wrist, and tugs me with her, off the porch and into the dusty backyard. 'Come sit with me.'

Your mother knows everything about me, Little One. She's good at comforting people, too, but you know that already. As much as I want to see pieces of myself reflected in you, I hope that you'll inherit this part of her.

She wraps me in her arms again, and we sit, watching the lights in the sky enact their spinning celestial ballet. Most of them are satellites, a few might even be shuttles for the Mars program. It's been so long since I lifted my eyes from the crumbling dust of these fields, that I forget how multitudinous the lights have become. They all look like stars to my untrained eye, having come unfixed from their eternal places in the heavens.

'We're going to make something new for her.' She means you, Little One. And she's right – even as she says it, I know she is. We might have to live in the undersea colony for fifty years or five hundred while the Earth above tries to heal, but I know that one day you'll come back to the surface, maybe even to this spot.

We're making something new for you. That's why we're going to a place with no sun, a place far from our family's land. We'll give you a fighting chance, even if it means redefining everything that we've come to understand about ourselves. I can study plankton farming, and your mother can teach you the names of fish instead of land animals. Together, we'll re-make the world for you.

Kelly Davis
The Last Lioness

People buy tickets,
wait in snaking queues,
to see the queen
brought low:
The Last Lioness.
They can say
          they were there,
took photos
          on their phones.

In her cage, She is haunted
by the scent
          of prey,
tastes the bubble of blood
at the antelope's mouth,
sees the hooves kicking,
the sliver of life
          snatched away.

Now there is only
          pacing, pacing,
the slow draining of days.
Eyes that scanned the savannah
brought up short
          by walls.
Meat arrives   in buckets.

Karen Ankers
Touch

Hold your children's screen-numbed fingers, glide
their touch over fur and feathers, still them
for anxious birds to feed, close them tight around
scattered seeds, warm them in folds of
slackened skin, mark them with
mud and dough and ink, dip them
in clay and blood-warmed paint, teach them
to feel and draw and tell
silenced stories bound by words.

Untutored fingers clasp cold screens, dance
over keypads before they trace
initials on a lover's skin, scrabble at scraps
in frozen ground, jerk in search of patterned codes,
remember too late we are more than bones,
skin-wrapped and numbered, bred to buy, taught to
want
from first breath to last, laden with
things we will never need, unable to touch
each other's hands.

Angela Graham
Because I Have Been Complacent About Climate Change

Winter is senile. He has forgotten how, in my childhood home,
my mother would sift ashes over the evening's embers,
smooring them flat with the shovel-back to keep the essential in.
He must have been watching her, for in the mornings I'd find a
warm core
and on the inside of every windowpane the sweep of Winter's palm
where he'd breathed his dreams onto the glass and sealed them in
– his cherished paradises: hushed ice-forests, heavily, deeply rich.
Now, in December, the postman's in shorts, snow an urban myth
and Winter has bedded down with the homeless and the
poor, dreamless,
bewildered, mumbling to passers-by that I abandoned him.
But how can I atone? There are no freezing drifts to trudge
through
barefoot, as an emperor once did to repent his abuse of power.
I'll be a servant of the edges, to restore Winter to his right mind
and rightful sway – and my home to a time / season balance.

Ness Owen
Note To Self

Rip up your lawn
plant a garden,
buy an apple

with a blemish
and park your car.
Stop wasting time

pointing your finger
stop buying things
fashioned to break.

Understand, this time
next year will be worse.
Teach these lessons.

Teach our children.
Learn what we forgot.
Be the truth-teller

waking early, catching
the first bird to take
up their song. Mother

earth is always speaking.
If you're waiting for
a sign, this is it.

Tim Dillon
Chronoflight

The following document is believed to have originated in the United
States in the late 21st century, prior to the Silicon Age Collapse.

Earth has gone to Hell, but your life doesn't have to. You
have been chosen for your taste, discernment, and of course
means, to receive this special offer. Chronoflight is offering
select individuals an opportunity to live your life in luxury in
a pristine world, untouched by the ravages of climate change.
The future is bleak, but the past is idyllic, and now thanks to
our patented time travel technology, we can transport you
to one of our many chrono-sealed resorts in any number of
climates and eras.

The safety of our guests is our highest concern, and this
includes the safety of their pasts. Chronoflight's procedures
are based on the research of top theoretical physicists, using
carefully constructed timeline divergence models to prevent
time paradoxes which might have deleterious effects on reality,
and thus the existence of our guests. The first step in the
construction of any of our resorts is extensive consultation
with historians of the period, in order to ensure temporal
integrity. All of our resorts are constructed in uninhabited
locations from Earth's past, built out of materials shown to
leave no traces or residue. In addition, all waste is disposed
of internally, through highly efficient systems which recycle
99.99% of all matter and energy.

Earth's past is host to all sorts of pristine environments, and there's no reason why those who can afford it shouldn't enjoy the very best this planet has to offer. Whether you want an untouched boreal forest, Arctic ice, or a beach as clean as the day it formed, we promise that we can find you a new environment that's entirely to your taste.

Within the facilities themselves you will find luxury accommodations, including food by Michelin star chefs, the latest in zero g spas, and spacious rooms. With the whole history of the whole planet to choose from, our resorts are built to take advantage of the plentiful real estate. Depending on the era of your choice, you will also be able to choose from a selection of tours, including a dinosaur safari, a submarine ride through the primordial oceans, or even up close viewings of all sorts of natural disasters, all of which are entirely safe for our guests.

Consider Chronoflight; because your future may be in Earth's past.

Lucy Grace
After This

After this,
I'm going to speak of all the things
We no longer have.

All the things
We no longer point at, saying –

                            Look!
                            Look at that!

Later
We will not know
Where everything went.
We will look at each other, saying –
                Remember those massive spiders that came
                          out from behind the telly?
            Remember how those bees loved your lavender?
                      Remember flying ant day?

We will not remember why we ridded them.
We will not remember
that spiders were housekeepers and fat bees were lifesavers
and ants built their communities under our feet.

In the shed
Under the sink
Beneath the stairs
We will secretly gather old killing sprays and suffocating powders,
embarrassed by ourselves.

After this,
I'm going to speak of all the things
We still have.

Lisa Clarkson
These Days

He does not cry, even as I flick
leeches from his wrinkled toes,
leaving round red kisses,
the only kisses we can risk
these days.
The sky is dark with swarms
of insects – loud, aggressive clouds.
We follow their patterns on the news,
close windows, stay inside and wait
for them to find us anyway.
We spend a long time waiting
these days.
He used to have a voice, but he asked
too many questions I couldn't answer.
We don't talk much
these days.
But at night, while I listen to the rain,
count the drops, foretell floods –
imagine spiders scrambling up my skirts
seeking air –
I lie still and close my eyes.
Sometimes I dream, even these days,
that he can run without falling. Then
red peeling, crabs crawling under skin.
It's just a dream
these days.

I check on him in the dark
and cannot hear him breathing,
but know he lives by the smell
of sweat in his warm hair.
After school, I wipe soot
from his nostrils and pretend I'm glad
there won't be grandchildren.
No one hopes for that
these days.
But we don't say
we might have done better.
Spoken up, put our money
where our mouths
gaped.
We can't be certain of anything
these days.
I show him how to sort plastic
from glass,
watch them disappear
into a void that isn't there.
There is nowhere else,
these days.

Corinna Schulenburg
Glacier, Calve Slowly

Glacier, the last time
you were here you were mighty
vaster than all elephants
pale castle, glittering hill,
a Goddess who leaves stones behind
to find her way back.

Glacier, now you come
tiny as the nervous fingers of rain
slapping the edges of shore
like a girl who forgot how to dance
de-bulked, de-boned, so
de-throned you permit
the Moon, that far-away duchess,
to move you.

Glacier, we blather hot air
upon your majesty, make sick
the seasons upon which you once set
a watch that ticked, immaculate,
now the glass face cracks
and sets loose a thousand devils
that you kept from us
in the bright billows of your dress.

Glacier, calve slowly.
The mess we made of things
may yet be, must be, set right.
Descend your staircase
one step at a time, gown catching
the sun's fire in such a dazzle
that all the world shall love you
and lay the dirty machines down.

Mandy Macdonald
After Before

England is so much smaller now
than in your day. You ask how London is: well,
it's gone. It went slowly,
but it went. Did you not know,
up there in the Highlands?
We rowed out today
in the Corporation's survey boat
to take water samples
(research, you know, aka hindsight);

made fast to a strange little spike of old stone,
one of four, arranged in a square. Not your usual
high jagged peaks of iron and concrete,
twenty or more floors still showing, eyeless
and rusting, weathered in the salt air of the Delta.
Not many of those left; they were too tall, too
shallow-rooted; corners were cut, jobs skimped;
they collapsed. Still sending up messages, though:
methane bubbles, occasional slow-burbling slicks of oil,
plastic, plastic, plastic. How was it you guys
couldn't kick that habit?

Four small pinnacles, ornate, almost fussy,
barely surfacing; below them, through the water,
the long unbroken plesiosaur's back of a roof
(memo to self: check lead trace levels). Underneath,
a whole building, barnacle-clad,
though only divers can see it now.
I'd brought along one of those old paper maps
from Before, when the Thames was just a river,
London a great city proud on its banks,
and there it was: 'Southwark Cathedral'.

I remember cathedrals – remember, at least,
reading about them. Peering down,
I imagined jewelled glass fragments carpeting
the delta floor, columns and vaulting now
a true forest, kelp sinuous among the trunks.

Rachael Li Ming Chong
The Flooding

one day the river
bloated and rain swollen
defied the maps
and all the dreams of meander
burst into adjacent fields
to acquire a new torso

and in its new waters
were submerged bales of hay
rolled cylinders
peeling at its cross-section
fish darting through alfalfa strands
inconvenienced by the presence
of such oversized ornaments

there were wild flowers too
swaying in the undercurrents
aquatic buttercups, knapweed, sorrel
hawk's beard, dandelion, fairy flax
also the purple gingham of fritillary
ready for picnicking
especially by bees
they paddled through
wings silvery oars
stirring up ripples that widened
to paint the shore pollen

and the plain sieved the sediment
and the plain locked the carbon
into treasure chests of soil
and still said *pour the buckets*
re-route the streams, I'll hold more

turn the cogs anti-clockwise
with our fingers, wind the sun
forward into mechanical view
and the waterlog will turn
to marsh will turn to meadow
where the grass undulates
to the movement of fish
whose bones ground to dust
scaffold the earth

Rob Walton
Mr King Has Decided To Pursue Other Avenues

It was a liberal and progressive school – some would say slack and lackadaisical – and when Mr King said he wanted to stay at the beach at the end of the trip, they wished him well and happily set off without him. It was almost time for the long holiday, and when he wasn't there to take registration the following morning they arranged temporary cover, and later replaced him with somebody younger with a similar name and the same tattooist. (Mr Prince would be pleased to get the job because Hokusai's expertly inked *The Great Wave off Kanagawa*, which covered all of his back, had been very expensive. And quite painful. Also, he knew it would be a star turn on a staff night out.)

Throughout his life Mr King had been reluctant to leave the beach when others decided it was time to go. He recalled sweating parents carrying him up steep steps at King Edward's Bay when he was really too old to be carried by anyone. He still wondered whether his teenage engagement had been broken off because of his insistence on rebuilding the top edge of a moat with damper sand, rather than catching the 2-for-1 cocktails on Front Street.

Now, as a fully-grown adult, three years into a middle-age-crisis job change and what was expected to be a fairly long career in teaching, he had walked away from his classroom and data-input responsibilities because he was in love.

He was in love with all the simple and obvious things, like the sea washing over him and the feel of the sand on his feet. He loved the smells and the sounds when the human visitors had gone home for the night. He loved the creatures and the dunes and the moonlight on the water. He loved the scent of what people thought was ozone. He knew it wasn't that, but his science was mostly experiential, and he didn't worry about names. This had got him into trouble one term when he referred to all the children in his class as either Child A or Child B, but those days were now behind him.

The first night he stayed at the beach, he lay flat between a favourite rock pool and the cliff face. He experimented and discovered piled bladderwrack makes an excellent pillow. As time went by, he found himself edging towards the rock pool and sleeping with his feet in it. He would smile in slumber, as hermit crabs scuttled around his ankles.

He got into the habit of hiding himself from view, and was blessed with an ability to merge into the landscape. He thought of camouflage and balance and symbiosis.

By the end of the summer, he slept wrapped around a rock in the middle of the pool, and as autumn came, he found he could quite easily slip under it for extra warmth.

He mostly stayed under this larger rock during the winter, but occasionally he'd emerge to see the dawn, and if the tide was right, he'd clamber round the headland to see the next bay at dusk.

Another night-time activity was clearing all manner of detritus from the beach. In his former job he'd have been able to collect it and take it to school for some work on sorting and discovering the properties of materials. *Which do you think would take longer to decompose: this crisp packet, this fishing line or this doll's leg? How could we find out? Come on, someone must have an idea? Do any of you care?*

His favourite after-dark task was sweeping the beach of footprints. The tide did this most of the time, but depending how that was turning, Mr King was always prepared to lend a helping hand. He did it because he wanted a pristine beach so children and others could walk on it the following day as though they were the first. He knew coastal erosion meant they would be some of the last, but he tried to concentrate on the positives.

He left the footprints of birds and other animals. He would stare and try to work out what they were. He didn't mind if he didn't know. He told himself if knowing was power, not knowing was wonder, and it was wonder he sought. But all the same he knew some things and he ought to use that knowledge.

As the days started to lengthen, he noticed changes in his skin and his bones. He could manoeuvre round all sorts of rocks now and could sometimes be in two pools at once. He loved this new quality but, like the thought-showered flexi-time at school, it didn't last.

He woke one day in the late spring to find this flexibility had deserted him to be replaced by quite the opposite. His upper body became scaly and, from his hips down, he started to calcify. He found it increasingly hard to tear himself off the rocks in the morning. He didn't know whether he should try.

He did try. He realised he had to. If things stayed as they were, the tides would come, and the tides would come again, and the beaches would flood. The great wave would come and there was nowhere for the water to go. There wasn't a natural landscape behind the beach. There was the new equivalent of the cocktail bars he'd rejected as a younger man. There were tall apartment buildings with much sought-after views of the climate crisis, although the estate agents phrased it slightly differently.

He decided he wanted to be neither calcified nor under water. He thought of people being petrified, people drowning, and he thought of parasitism which couldn't continue.

He thought of the misrepresented Cnut of a thousand years ago. Another King trying to prove that he couldn't in fact control the tides, the seas, the oceans. There was a story, like so many others, that had been twisted. He thought of making a sand throne as a last hurrah and shouting at the waves, but knew it would raise a wry smile and do no good.

As spring turned to summer, he was aware of school parties visiting and he started to think of his old class and colleagues. They were all a year older, and had been in countless lessons, but he wondered if he was the only one who was a year wiser.

He'd tuned in to moons and tides and seas and, while he didn't think it was how everybody should live, he knew it was important and he had to tell people. He thought he might leave out a few parts, claim he'd been at an aunt's in Bergen or an uncle's on Orkney. He knew he had to get the bus back to school, try to remember some of the children's names and talk to them about their future.

Samn Stockwell
Betty Always Sees Herself From A Distance

as though she stood behind herself,
slightly to the right – in her mind's eye, but
why does the mind have a separate eye?

Her other eyes are bleary
with reading into the night by a smidgen of light.
How do people sleep in the incessant hammering
of a world dying? Is that the mind's ear?

She puts her hands over her mouth
but not her ears. She wants to reach into
people's tin ears and rip them open.
Now can you hear us?

She has marked some trees
for logging because they are unsound.

Samn Stockwell
She Notices The Giant Grate Tilted

over the drain – the town road flooded
and spring tracing the good mud
she stands in, black boots patched.

Betty tracks into her kitchen.
The good mud is the wealth left her.
She sweeps out the effluvium
of a life parsed by a single path.

Sawdust and leaves are tamped
at the base of the rhubarb and
the squash seedlings. (*And if the rain
extinguishes the rest of the soil, then what?*)

The cold is reverberating
under the chilly branches of the oak
and she's the only one out in this,
buying the last seed at the store, dripping
on the floorboards, and inhaling
the joy of her solitary return,
a landscape lit in greys.

Lesley Curwen
Views Of Greenland From Seat 39A

a second bloody mary crackles
I imagine bergs sweating to bits
in carbon-knit jumpers

see the curved bay blown
by a thousand blues
moving jewel
spotted and dotted
by blobs and slabs
oblong or liner-like   sharp prows
decks   a   mile   long
a sight to dismay lookouts
fleet with no crew   no compass
no heading   no sails

how long does it takes to melt
diamond-dirt bodies   to flush them
down the bowl of Labrador Sea

who knew that dilution of water
by water would murder plankton
for want of plankton   whales expire

I am looking out for whales
they are invisible from this height
too far away to be real

Katherine Gallagher
The White Boat

(After a Students' *Save Our Environment* Exhibition)

The child's world
is born on a white boat

but these children have fixed on
dead birds and dead suns,
a *papier-mâché* baby wailing
and paper-trees
littered with old cartons,
cigarette-packs,

everything documented
without magic or mercy:

their multiple-voice shrilling

It spits in your eye
an anti-revolution
dropping warnings over plugged-up rivers
as a frilly lady smiles papery
out of the crumpled span of her hat

and the last white boat
sticks on a black canal.

Jessica Conley
Erosion

You have never
watched a balsam
fir fall into
First Lake but have
seen their roots
clutching at what is
left of the small
islands. Fingers reach
for any hold.
Bare roots knot from
the shore into
the water where brown
bullheads swim
beneath their arcs.
In the beaver meadow,
the soft curve of
adder's tongue leaves
sprout from
what was once
a dam. You pick
wild flowers for your
kitchen window before
nightfall arrives
in the Adirondacks.
Environmentalists studied
the islands and now
warn people
not to walk on

their loamy shores.
You read it in the paper,
but you and your
grandfather
already knew.
A loon wails at dusk.
Then, the rains
wash away sand
and soil surrounding
the sarsaparilla.
There is nothing
left to hold.
The environmentalists
will plant more
mosses. In the morning,
you watch a white-tailed
buck swim to one
of the islands
to graze on
fungi and trillium.
The ski boats will
be out soon, churning
the lake with waves.
Your grandfather
readies the canoe
while the water
is still. As you row,
your oar dips
into the clouds, and below
the mirror's surface,
a fallen tree slick
with algae
darkens the lake.

Stevie Krayer
Recharting The Territory

Where are we? Song-lines, archipelagos
of knots in twine, little fleets
of outriggers weaving the world
into a cradle, letting sea and land
show us where we stood. We turned,
reverently ochred the landscape
with what we needed it to mean.

You are here. Later, emboldened,
we drew our mappae mundi without looking:
us and our special places at the centre
of everything. The authorities
were slow to take down the city walls
and see the truth of the lie of the land.
Easier to erase the truthtellers.

This land is our land: We-know-best grandees
in topees and top hats, in offices and map-rooms
built, tunnelled, razed, dumped,
drawing confident lines across continents,
dividing and ruling, shifting whole peoples
with hunger and bombs, posting an alien label
on someone's home and then evicting them.

Recalculating... Goaded beyond retrieval
Nature has uninstalled Inkscape
and is taking our sloppy handiwork
to its last flourish. Google Maps shall be wiped.

With all its apocalyptic tools – fire, famine,
meltwater, microscopic armies, mass extinction –
Earth is taking back control.

Perform a U-turn where possible.

Diana Powell
Memory Of Snow

This. Then.

The child, eyes rapt, tongue furled up, out, to catch a spark of ice. To taste, feel it explode into frozen emptiness. To catch again, to run, to catch. This.

Her.

You. How old were you, then, you wonder? Searching for clues in the clothes you were wearing, the height of the child, measured against the trees. Was there anyone with you? A grown-up? Other children?

Children laugh, now, when you tell them such things, when you tell them about snow.

Five years? Eight years? Ten? No, not ten, ten is too old. Because, of course, it is from *before*, from *then*. Before Ragnarök... The End of the World. That is what some have taken to calling it, looking back on that time.

You laugh at this. As if Odin, Thor, all the Aesir, did battle with Loki, the giants, the monsters. Stories the Ancestors told, when gods occupied the earth, fought over it, and brought about its destruction, breaking the surface open, causing flood and fire to wreak havoc throughout the lands. Nonsense! It was no such thing!

And yet... the water keeps on rising to the south. And here, in the north – no flames, maybe, but a heat hotter than ever imagined, climbing day by day.

So... *The end of the world as we knew it* is fair enough. Done, while men occupied the earth. Men have done this.

This: A hare lopes in front of you, stops, catches you in its stare.

An etch across the snow. A hasty shading. Only the movement, the glint of its eye reveals it. White on white. Breath taken away by their matching perfection.

When you were still small enough to lift on her knee, your grandmother told you stories about the white hare, with its magic coat, how it was a shape-shifter, a trickster. Your grandmother's stories were gentler than the Ancestors', peopled by animals with human names, who did human things. So there were tales of the other creatures, too. The caribou. The wolves. The owl. Stories for dark winter nights… so many of them, through the weeks and months of half a year. They were something to entertain you, until the sun rose again.

The hare was one of the old woman's favourites. You are glad she has gone now, does not know these dull, muddy creatures, matching a dull, muddy landscape.

She loved the ice-bears, too. The bears have gone now. Something else you are pleased about, glad she has not seen them disappear, one by one.

You get up, gather your Thermo-meter, your Perma-drill, your Micro-pad; pull on your grass-rollers, head back to town. No need for skis, now, not without snow.

This. The shushing of the blades through the powder. A movement through the air, a rushing. Down, down; on, on. Flying. She is flying. And this. Lace slung across the branches of the pines, sewn by their needles. Or… 'Are they cobwebs? The cobwebs of giant snow-spiders?' She reaches up, touches, her finger following the threads, dissolving them as she goes. Magic.

51

And this. The silence. The hush. What it does... A smothering, the clamp of hands to her ears... her, looking all around, searching for a noise that must be there. That bird, racing across the valley, the wind whistling through it? That snowmobile she sees on the ridge. But there is nothing, they are there, but not there. The snow has taken their voices. The snow itself is silence.

Until... not that night. It was the sound you heard, first. They all heard first, they said later, waking them from their beds, those who were asleep. Those who were dead. The Dead woken by it, too. Something you didn't see – you have seen them since, seen the graves open, the coffins splintered apart, the arms reaching up. The faces, looking for something, someone, the ones they want to return to. But not then, they were kept from you then. You were only a child, after all.

Your mother's hand, grabbing your own, pulling you from the house. You, the other children, outside, rubbing sleep from your eyes, to look at each other, not understanding. Then looking behind... at the noise. You watched the houses trundle down the street, thought you were dreaming. Rubbed your eyes again.

Rain – there had been rain. Grey, wet, heavy. Falling day after day, when it should not fall. No-one liked the rain, dredging across the Sugar Top, soaking it to the skin, then skimming it in ice, when the freezing came. Then...

Snow. 'The wrong kind of snow'. The weight of it, finding nowhere to sink in to, gathering, moving, pushing. A wave. Reaching the town, reaching the homes, climbing through windows, climbing upstairs, reaching the beds. Drowning those too slow to move, or those who had no mothers to grab their hands.

Most were lucky, they said. At first.

This was when it began. 'The day begins when you wake up' – one of your grandmother's sayings. She had a lot to say when the snow-dust settled, when the clean-up was over, when the grown-ups, as well as the children, rubbed the sleep out of their eyes, and faced the new dawn. And more stories from her, not so gentle, now. The fox, this time. How its long, full brush swept the surface of the snow, sending up sparks, to set off the lights. The lights had been at their brightest that winter. 'An omen. A doom!' The lights in her stories were never kind – her, telling us not to wave at them, telling us to stay indoors.

'Don't look!' But how could we not?

Dark, yet not dark. The maidens come, wrapped in their flouncing gowns, their rainbow scarves trailing down. They dance, their skirts curtseying onto the white veil, the red, the purple, the green playing with it, as they sashay along. A spiral, a twirl back up, around the snow-capped mountains, swirling between them, hugging them, kissing them, now, closer, close, then back to her, wanting to take her hand. 'Don't look,' her grandmother had told her. How could she not look? How could she not dance with them, as they lit up the snow?

'Grandma needs something to blame. She's trying to understand,' your mother said, 'to make sense of it in her own way.' Making sense of your grandfather, her dead husband rising from the ground, as the permafrost melted; making sense of being moved from her life-long home; of the cemetery being moved. Of being moved again. 'Evacuated! As if we are at war.' Which we were. Just not the kind she remembered.

'She doesn't understand about rising temperatures, ice

melting, the sea disappearing. She's too old!'
Others, younger, learnt. Too late.

The town is quiet, now. Quieter than that night, when the whole population gathered, to help those injured, to save what could be saved. Quieter than the years that followed, decade after decade. A slipping away...

The houses moved back, by intent, this time. Those evacuations. The graves, the graveyard, shifted, with all its dead. They tried, they adjusted. Worked hard, did their best. But... too late. And what is this place without snow?

They slipped away, as they had done in the past. The Sami. The whalers, the miners, the tourist guides, hoteliers and their staff, the dog sledders. The Sami, again. The wildlife. Only scientists come here now, to measure, to analyse, to record. To hope: You.

You stand on the edge of the quay, waiting to be picked up, looking out at the sea, which is no longer YOUR sea, the one that used to be there. The busy port is busy no longer, the few ships in the bay are research vessels, one of them yours. The fishing boats, the tourist craft, are long gone. The influx of cod, herring and mackerel was welcomed at first, but did not last. The novelty of cruising to the North Pole quickly faded.

The sea has gone, the ocean it flowed into has gone.

'How can an ocean disappear?' people asked. But it did. Drowned by a bigger, warmer, saltier one.

'How can whole islands sink?' But they have, swallowed by the water surrounding them.

'How can there be no snow anymore?'

But there isn't.

You shake your head at the thought of it. You shake your head, wanting to shake your memories away. Like a snow globe in reverse, you think. Shaking, to get rid of the white flakes filling the air, filling a child with wonder. Wanting them to float to the bottom of your mind, where they stay hidden. But...

This. She stands there, in the middle of a white world, white, as far as she can see, turning this way, that. The purity of it. She, the tiniest dot in the middle of it all, in the middle of the world. Feeling she is nothing. She does not matter at all. THIS is what matters. The land. The sky above. This earth around her. This is what the snow does.

This is what memory does.

And for this, you will still try.

Claire Booker
Mr McGregor's Seedlings

Rosy-faced Kilner jars twinkle from all points
of his kitchen – some things, at least, can be bottled.

He forks air into what has been achieved: his soft fruits
win prizes; their yield is the envy of the allotment.

Soil possesses him – the rub and tilth of it.
Its endless riddles invade his fingers.

He's dug a small pond by the lean-to, where he rests
with his flask in the company of frogs –

reads about poisoned bees, plundered peat bogs,
herbicides that strip the land of worms.

On weekdays, voices from the infant school hop over,
lively as crickets. Next month he'll give a talk –

take little pots to plant enthusiasms; unpack a sunflower
to show its eager heart.

Tara Willoughby
Humidity

A forty-two (42) degree day and
the air at the YMCA pool is
eight (8) degrees cooler but
eight thousand (8000) percent more humid.
All the tweens running around stink –
a combination of chlorine and the first
hints of body odour.
All the babies are sticky.

The kiosk is doing a roaring trade
in icy poles and hastily pulled
espresso shots drowned in milk.
My iced coffee would be bitter
if it wasn't fifty (50) percent vanilla syrup.
I came here to swim laps,
swimmers under my tank top and shorts,
but I am one hundred (100) percent done.

On the drive home, I hold my breath
until the cigarette butt, flicked out the
window of the car two (2) spots ahead of me at
the lights, goes out. I can't bear this
tension. I stop at a muddy creek, not
a river at this time of year, and paddle my feet.
There are tiny fish swarming in the shallows.
I don't know how many.

Ben Macnair
Yellow Brimstone

It was the briefest of moments,
A flash of yellow against the bluest of skies.
A Yellow Brimstone, a butterfly
probably less than a week old,
taking to the air.
It was rare, so we noticed,
but a Cabbage White was flashier,
a Red Admiral more photogenic,
just for a moment,
a Yellow Brimstone flew past,
said I am here,
notice me,
and we did.

Natascha Graham
Weather For Politicians

The sea curls back
Like the lip of the woman next to me
Whose straight white teeth bite
Plastic straw
And tanned hand holds plastic cup
Whilst she says
It's hot, but it'll get hotter
In an accent stretching from place to place
Between Paris and Morocco
And we sit
Backs to the sky
Faces to the sand
Where, in the dazzle of sunshine on surf
A boy pokes the eye of a rotting turtle
With a stick
Its body twice his size, rising and falling with the waves
A dull brown hump in the hot gold sand
With a glittering plastic collar

AG Parker
This Rewilding Wind

This wind has come
to sweep the tremblings of mountains,
the shudder of far-distant stars
into my heart,
to bear longings of peat and wood smoke and valley air into
my lungs.

This wind comes with the richness of the blood of the
setting sun
as it sets fire
to hidden pastures.

This wind comes to scatter the notes
of a willow's song into my hair,
to leave ocean spray clinging to my skin,
to blow the cracks in a cloud-fettered sky into the caves of
my eyes.

This wind comes
with the roar of the desert,
to smooth my bones
with the roughness of its tongue
to keep them strong
and honed and ready.

This wind has come
to kindle fire in my heart,
salt the blood in my veins,
lace the tread of my step
with the power of ancient ways
that are spun and bundled around the land
and back into my body.
This wind has come
in the name of rewilding.

Lyndsey Weiner
Occupy Frogs

In the dream my son
is drowning.
When I wake up the frogs laugh
their deep throaty ribbit
through the screen door. *You think*
you could have saved him
they croak. *When our pond was sick*
with algal bloom you went out
and bought an air conditioner.
The neighbours say it's God's plan.
Either way we are boiling.

Cath Holland
For Sale. One Planet. Well Worn.

Sale No. 127b.
Exact proportions and statistics are as follows:

Mass	5.9736×1024 kg
Mean diameter	12,742 km
Surface area	510,072,000 km2
Density	5.515 g/cm3
Circumference	40,041 km
Human population	7,800,000,000

For 4.343 billion years, this item was a detached, much loved family home. Over the last 200,000 years a change in ownership saw the development and successful exploitation of all its natural resources. As a result, the item has excellent provenance and boasts a long and varied history of productive negotiations involving religion, oil and power, ensuring peace breaks out in regular intervals.

The human population, which is included in the sale, is a major asset, and flourishes within the planet's economic business model. Service industries are a very strong sector in urban and highly populated areas. In the UK alone, call centre workers produce 1.3 tonnes of CO^2 emissions each year through their commutes, reflecting their sheer numbers and an unbridled enthusiasm for a career in customer service. In surviving the Great Plague Year of 2021, citizens of reproductive age have proved themselves to be resilient, and reliable members of the workforce. Flexible employment contracts allow citizens substantial and welcome freedoms.

The population effectively controls and disciplines itself through the popular practice of classism, misogyny, disablism, racism and homophobia. To assist these shared common values, legislation counteracts any threat or possibility of behaviour outside accepted social norms. Laws are fast-tracked when necessary.

However, it is prudent for an investor to be aware of any problem areas of possible concern, and act accordingly. For example, online petitions generated by any individual or group of citizens can be largely dismissed, but any new buyer is advised to rubber stamp the occasional animal abuse complaint.

Social media outrage much like troublesome citizens is easily cancelled. Violations of community standards are dealt with swiftly. Halting public transport during rush hour has been a recent climate change protest phenomenon proving problematic. However, if citizens arrive late for work in the morning and use the following excuses – held up by a demonstration, childcare problems, illness or death in the family – this now results in immediate dismissal.

Full disclosure – Article 4 of the Sale Regulations Code dictates any past activity which might, *in theory*, affect future prospects of any sale must be shared with potential investors and shareholders. Because of this, details of decreases in the size of waters and landmasses are attached. However, be assured the decrease is in fact encouraging news, as medium to long term, such changes create ample space open to a multitude of uses and business opportunities. Insurance companies are reluctant to cover certain geographical locations, but those areas will not be an issue long term due to depletion. Earth is freehold, a massive plus. You can do what you want with it. However, citizens and industry have worked together to iron out minor concerns around environmental issues.

To run a 'paperless office', any paper use can be offset by replacing proportional use with a single planted sapling. It will take several years to grow to full size, but its PR value is extremely high. Use the colour green in any logos and promotional material, and the image of a tree. This wins top approval from citizens, along with takeaway food and withdrawal of foreign aid. Car ownership by citizens is socially essential.

Restaurants serve single-use disposable plates, cups and cutlery instead of washing ceramic, stainless steel, glass; citizens respond favourably to this. They enjoy the warmer summers, milder winters and don't mind that spring never arrives anymore. Atheism is popular except for a period in late December when citizens en masse patriotically boost the western economy. This should be further encouraged. Lung conditions such as asthma are commonplace in the children of citizens, but this is easily dismissed as a natural phenomenon due, ironically, to the very commonality of the disease.

Planet Earth has so much potential for the right buyer. We are so pleased to broker this investment opportunity, as rare as the Tasmanian tiger (extinct 1936), golden toad (1989), and West African black rhinoceros (2011). There is plenty of natural ultraviolet light; between two and three million non-melanoma skin cancers and 132,000 melanoma skin cancers occur globally each year. This opens up an increased market for new pharmaceutical industries.

For further disclosure, a history of plagues of blood, frogs, insects, wild animals, pestilence, boils, hail, locusts, darkness and death of newborns indicate the population may have needed at some point in the past, discipline from an outside force. Interested parties can dismiss this as a future threat. Frogs, any insects with more than four legs, 90% of mammals and birds, and all locusts, are now extinct, so in the unlikely event that history repeats itself, consequences will be minimal.

As predicted there has been strong interest in Sale No. 127b. The asking price, however, can be negotiated for quick sale.

Xia Leon Sloane
Flood Warning

twelve bells swell
throats raw
with the hoarse stillness
of a winter morning –
they have been cast,
sly, swift
fishing nets, to catch
the whole sky's tolling
as it races its own embers
to tangle in their tight, bright
mesh landing the brittleness
of clouds, wombs of rain
nest, dark birds swollen
and silent –
an old church
bell; awakening
rivers, they strip armfuls of time
like nectar
from flowers

Katherine Gallagher
The Year Of The Tree

I carried a tree
through the Underground.

It was hard. At first,
people scarcely noticed me

and the oak I was lugging
along the platforms –

heavier than a suitcase
and difficult to balance.

We threaded through corridors,
changing lines: up and down stairs,

escalators, and for a moment
I imagined everyone on the planet

taking turns
to carry a tree as daily rite.

A few people asked
Why a tree?

I said it was for my own
edification –

a tree always
has something to teach.

   ***

Sharp gusts
whirred through the corridors

rustling the branches
as I hurried on

past the sweepers
picking up rubbish, scraps of paper.

Be sure to take the tree
with you, they said.

Don't worry, I'm taking it
to my garden,

the start of a forest.
When people stared,

Relax, I said,
it's a tree, not a gun.

Kate Foley
Now And Then

When the sun has folded
the sheet of sky,
it's then we know
that birds are music.
They fill the night
with eight-bar rests.

Morning –
and language
floods between leaves
and chimney pots.

The whole sky
is pencilled
with swift strokes.

Long before the first
handprint smudged
a cave wall
birds knew
how to sing,
speak –
fling
their breasts
and wings
into the waiting
gallery of air.

Now a hope, fragile
as a thrush's egg,
that when our broken cities,
are one day
covered by silent
rosebay willow herb,
the birds' long
history of art
survives.

Robert René Galván
Dominion

Who can say how the weaver bird
builds his mansion
from a thousand blades of grass,
the warp and weft
of his ebony beak
for the prospect of love;

or how the foal unfolds
from her wet heap
and trembles to her feet,
ready to take her place
in the field of thistles
and wild yarrow;

or how the tadpole evades
the mandibles of the dragonfly larva,
unaware that he will soon become
a frog and exact revenge
with his darting tongue;

or how the lumbering leatherback,
an angel in the water,
returns to the same sand
to bury her clutch year after year,
or how the egret knows
when the feast will hatch on the shore;

or how the hornet's silo
emerges from saliva and pulp
and from a pair of ganglia,
and likewise, the hosts
of butterflies navigate
a continent from a bundle
in the thorax;

and how our own pale progeny
arrive writhing and helpless
to assume dominion.

Kelly Davis
What The Natterjack Toad Teaches Us

When their sand dune pools
dry out entirely,
they burrow down into the soil.

Unable to jump or hop,
they run or crawl,
but still reach their destination.

Vulnerable to predators,
many toadlets become food for gulls.
The survivors are the ones who hide.

Their numbers shrink,
they become scattered,
but their calls reach across the miles.

When they mate,
the world shrinks to two bubbled backs
rocking in unison.

Many eggs are lost
but some turn into tadpoles
flicking through the water, fiercely alive.

Lucy Ryan
Asteraceae

Daisy liked it best buried beneath the mud. She heard the call to be covered over vibrating through the earth and renamed herself, buried one day with nothing but her head poking out from it, cheeks blistered red from the sun.

Her uncle Tommy had done it too a couple of decades before, digging holes in the yard like an excitable Labrador, but rarely burned so badly. The ozone was thicker then. The heat less harsh.

She had read about it in the library, the spiritual section pulling her as keenly as the mud had: to recharge the energy of a crystal you had to place it in the earth under the light of a full moon. That night she grasped at a new middle name, *Sapphire*, and sank into the flowerbed, beside the lavender, waiting for the calcium and carbon in her body to revitalise.

She would dig until her shoulders ached, the skin over the blunt end of her elbow-joint grazed and bruising, the missing limb hardly slowing her; dig until her body vibrated, edges loose and blurring, until she could be any shape she preferred. It became a ritual, grounding as meditation, to let the garden hold her close, hold her down.

Her mother had been worried, always worried, holding Daisy's hand like it was a wound she had to hold closed, the stump at the end of her left elbow a simple fact, her new name and hair and clothes a harder knot to untangle. But the kids were good. Daisy called herself *Daisy*, and so did everyone else. Her chin permanently jutted, jaw so often set; when she ran through the undergrowth, a gaggle of Neverland children were rarely far behind.

They didn't feel it like her, the buzz from below, the hum of the earth a constant rumble in her blood, but they ran, anyhow, seeds spilling from between stubby fingers. Daisy tilted her throat back and directed the shape of it, listening to the thrum of the earth shifting beneath her.

It was a feral summer when the storms came. Flash flooding. Thunder cracks. Every hole Daisy dug caving in with a wet slosh.

After the treehouse got struck by a particularly nasty lightning bolt, her mum had to hold her back by the shoulders to stop her skidding into the yard again. A smoky char swelled in the air for a week.

'You'll get struck,' she said. 'A branch'll come down and cave your soft little skull in.'

The lavender was long drowned, like everything else. The only stalwarts the tenacious little fuchsia heads, drooped and dripping, petals hanging off like severed limbs.

'Storms are getting worse every year,' her granddad said, shaking himself off like an unsteady whippet and clapping her on the shoulder. His gnarled fingers flicked disapprovingly at the length of her hair. 'Never used to gush like this when we were boys. Worst we ever got was a couple power cuts –'cept that one lad that got struck playing knock down ginger.' He collapsed into the big chair, the curved, soft-worn velvet armchair they called *Granddad's Chair* even when he wasn't there.

Her mum clipped him softly round the back of the head, but eyed Daisy uneasily anyway.

Her knees hadn't been scuffed up in weeks, no moss stains

or filth. The rain was thick and smelled sickly-sweet.

'Why's it getting worse?' Daisy asked, fingers bunching in her shorts, pulling at where the material clung, sweat-slick, to her skin.

He laughed, a spluttering half-sound. 'Why's water wet? Why's mud brown?'

But she knew that one, mineral deposits, rich earth tended over and over by the animals that lived and died on it, replenishing the carbon with their slow decay.

'We got too clever for our own good,' he continued, croaking over the words with an emphysemic burble. 'Telly an' cars an' plastic an' all that. Greedy little buggers, people are.'

Daisy peeled the sodden fabric of her top away from her armpit, skin feeling hot and pins-and-needles sharp. 'I don't like it,' she said. 'It smells and it's dragging the ground away.'

'We done the messin',' he told her, touching her cheek, the skin of his thumb hard and flaking. ''s on you lot to fix it.'

She tilted her chin up then, her one small hand balled into a tight little fist. 'I will,' she told him, voice a low determined growl.

*

Next summer, Daisy was a head taller and still aching from the growth spurt, limbs loose and unfocused in their movement. A honey-warm tan slick across her skin. Difference sat determinedly on her shoulders, sure as her shadow in the thick midday sun.

She had only ever half-liked the fairy tales, the parts where girls hemmed close to the trees, animal confidantes trailing their shadows, but never the taming and lacing up of their edges. So she built her own strange, sprawling wilderness in the manicured yard, holes dug deep, and seeds sewn. A curl of land deftly reclaimed by the earth, swollen with green and shimmering flashes of colour. A place humming with magic, possibility stumbling on her tongue the same way her name used to, a solid thing she would bend herself to better fit. Ivy crept up the back wall, the floating layer of foliage making it appear as though the garden rolled on forever.

Even her mother would admit, peering from the kitchen door, cigarette drooping between her fingers, that the air felt easier to breathe out there.

The storms came back, of course, the change in temperament as sharp as the crags of the coastline, or the harsh slash of white at the front of her mouth that was Daisy's latest peeking adult tooth, but the overhanging trees bracketed the garden from the worst.

They watched it from the doorway, her mother's arms loose around Daisy's shoulders. The rain came in sheets and sluiced off the thick leaves, puddling the ground marshy and brown. The flowers were whipped by the wind, bursts of fluttering colour cast across the garden like diving butterflies.

Daisy began to tug, her teeth sunk into her lower lip, watching the flowers burst apart in the storm.

'*Daisy*,' her mother said, arms closing tighter.

But she kept pulling, flinching when a marigold head severed and slapped against the window. 'I have to –'

'Stop it,' her mother said, voice hardening, her knuckles white around Daisy's shoulder. 'It's not safe out there.'

'Exactly,' Daisy whined, wriggling free, loose and bendy from her growth spurt. She was barrelling through the back door before her mother could catch the edge of her T-shirt.

The rain abraded her, pounding against her soft skin as she trudged through the swampy earth, mud swallowing her up to the knees, splashing as high as her cheeks. She remembered the fairy tales, the parts where the woods turned treacherous, tree branches snapping at the princesses, the earth trying to swallow them whole.

But Daisy knew the earth, the beckoning hum. At that moment it felt like a roar.

She trudged her way into the grove, the trees sheltering her from further assault and found it, the tiny terracotta pot Granddad had given her at her last birthday.

In it, wind-whipped, over-watered and tilted up as if searching for sun, was a handful of red gerbera daisies, unwilted, waiting to bloom.

Cradling them close to her chest, she slid back through the mud, the rain raking warm and harsh across her spine. She trudged as fast as she could, sinking into the puddles as they littered the garden until the end of her short arm met the handle of the back door.

Her mother had a towel around her before she stepped inside, hefting her whole body up and marching her into the bathroom.

'You'll be the bloody death of me, if you're not the death of your bloody self,' she said, voice breaking on the last word. 'You need to be careful, Daisy. You're more fragile than you think.'

Daisy lurched onto the side of the bath, body swaying and sweating and cold, and peeled the towel away.

She didn't say anything, just pulled out the pot and rested it on the side of the bath.

Her mother looked at her mud-streaked, headstrong menace of a child, and swallowed back the sharp feeling that had risen in her throat. 'It'll grow just as well inside,' she said, one hand carding through Daisy's hair, as the other turned on the hot tap. 'On the windowsill, in your bedroom, don't you think?'

'Only until the storms pass,' Daisy whispered, her throat grown hoarse. She peeled one red petal from the inside of her palm and dropped it into the running water. 'The ground will want her back.'

Michelle Penn
retablo for the deep ocean

the streets scare me sometimes
sirens, a keening that cuts
my sleep, pierces
my veins, leaves me bleeding quiet
all over the floor
       I'm telling you this because you made
           silence, you blew breath
       into the first person

       and tonight, I'm thanking you
for just once sending the sirens far
stretching them to the shore, sinking them
beneath tides, sound slipping past sunlit reefs
filtering through murk
tangled squid and gelatinous things
then deeper, beyond silver-skinned fish
shaped like hatchets and electric jellies
to the abyss where no light
can reach, where sea spiders creep
beneath the icy weight of water
unhurried by current or storm
and the sirens spreading
across silt, into the deepest
trenches, dispersing
like a chant

Jared Pearce
The Rain

And what was the rain?
It was relentless.
And the corn?
It was new, two leaves trying,
     row upon row so
     far I couldn't follow.
And the soil?
Sodden troughs, peaks ready
     to mush with their flags
     slapping on the wind.
And the rain?
It was shaping the Earth,
     the love in her hands
     was trying.
And the wind?
It brought the dark and the rain,
     it gave the corn rest.
And?
It chilled in the wet.
And the soil?
It was relentless—
     staying up or drowning.

The rain was relentless?
The soil was wet with rain,
      the flags of corn, up
      on the rows, shivered
      on the rain, in the wind
      brushing low.
And the rows?
They had no end or beginning—
      only the middle came
      swooping near me
      before the polka dots
      of its footsteps crossed
      the sodden dark.
And the rain?
It brought what it had
      and took what it had to.

Simon Brod
We Are Beach People

and our dead have been set in motion. In our parents' time
it was rare for a coffin to shift – the sand held firm in those
days – but now the ocean rises and buoys them all adrift. We
spend our lives in half-lands tending our dead, rescue them
where they stray, breaching the surf, some still whole, some
stove-in, flooded. We wade through slush, pummelled by rain
and sea-spray, find them half-afloat, load them on sleds, haul
them up the beach, carve new caskets and bury them afresh
in a drier place.

If we cannot care for our dead, what are we then? They are
all we have, that and the screech of gulls. They multiply as
our world shrinks. Someday soon we'll run out of beach and
our dead will be lost to the sea.

Cathy Lennon
The Inescapable Irony Of Protective Packaging

The dining table has halved, one end occupied by the polythene sheep of bubble wrap we cannot bear to throw away. Our children are grown and flown, out into a shrinking world that burns and drowns. So this plague-ridden winter we eat on our laps by the fire instead.

Somewhere, endless bales and rolls extrude to waiting trucks, while choking oceans gasp and heave up on a distant shore. We watch billionaires build rockets; ears cocked for our children's call.

Pop, pop, our fidgety fingers go. Pop, pop.

The air has gone.

The children too.

But the plastic has not.

Xia Leon Sloane
Spring

five red fledglings shiver
a promise of foliage
like a small, fleeting
flock of memories
of wind –
below, winter's blood peers,
shy and green like wing beats
through the feathery crinkles
of last night's frost, coaxing it
to splinter
dustily beneath the paws
of dawn as she crumbles softly
across the sky and melts like glass –
flakes once perched
on the creaking thinness
of branches have scattered, chased
by four hatchlings
and a frightened night

silence now
one last bird falls

Karen Ankers
Icarus

One day he'll be a white-winged graceful shape
in a blue-stained summer sky, but now
a speckled seagull cries, head low, follows
his mother, stumbles along
the ridge of a roof.

I am the only one watching. Should I care?
He's just a bird, his cries a sound among
many – nature, I'm told, is cruel;
he has to learn to toughen up, be strong. She flies away. He
cries. He'll learn.

But take away the wings and he's a child, screaming
the loss of being alone. Without feathers
his terror would be naked tearstained headlines
for a day.

Love starts with the cries of forgotten
birds. One day he'll grace the skies, his
voice the soundtrack of summer; wings
a frame for ice-creamed warmth,

too far above to see. We won't listen
to his warning; let him fly
too close to the sun to see the earth melt.

Jane McLaughlin
Volunteer

Flax, hemp, papyrus, teff.

These were the seeds they were sent out to find. Some of them did not return. Maybe they did not take enough water with them. Or footpads killed them for it. But some did come back, and we have enough to clothe and feed us. And a small amount of papyrus for writing and art.

The children are playing so happily today. Maya is five and Deneb seven. They are making patterns with sand and pretty pebbles. Our back yard is paved with clay bricks with a sand border. They have a little truck of olive wood that Jos made. It is afternoon and they are in the shadow of the wall that shields us from the sun for part of the day.

Jos is a toymaker. Toymaking is a Valuable Activity Class 2. Though not Essential like cultivating the plants or maintaining the solar cells; the Committee consider that play is important for the development of our children.

We live in a perfect closed system. Nothing goes in or out. The Well is the centre of everything.

The Committee is honest with us. They do not know how long the solar cells will last. Maybe a generation, maybe less. They do not know whether or when the Well will dry up. So they tell us: Follow the water rules strictly. If you have anything you do not need or anything left from what you make, take it to the Repurposing Centre.

Jos has made some wheeled animals from olive wood and a couple of jointed dolls. Sometimes he goes to the clay pit – there if you dig down a metre you will find clay. Mostly dried out now, but it can be worked with water when there is any in the communal tank – not all of it can be recycled. The heat of the day is enough to bake it, left out on the bricks of the yard. He has made dice, five-stones, chess pieces, checkers and other games. He is permitted to keep a few for Maya and Deneb but the rest go to the Sharing Centre.

Nothing goes in or out. Of course that is not quite true. The wind blows in seeds. Birds fly overhead and sometimes plants grow from their droppings.

And so I notice that a green shoot has appeared towards the end of the yard, sprouting up between the cracks of two bricks.

This must be reported. The Committee will monitor it. If such a plant produces any seed, fruit or fibre that can be used they may allow some water for it. But by then most of these chance arrivals have withered.

A good-looking young man called Galil arrives from the Committee. By this time it has thrown up some soft green leaves.

He studies the plant, measures it.

'Very nice. Let's see what it does. And you know the rule. No water yet. Absolutely no water. We are running short for the season already. As far as we can tell there has been no rain in the hills that feed the underground water. The well is down two metres on what we would expect at this time of year. And there are still people trying to get in, you know.'

I do not like to think of it. Or the sharp arrows of the sentries.

It grows a flower.

The flower has a cup-shaped crimson calyx; above that six spear-shaped petals of soft pink alternated with others striped cream and white. Inside a pale green pistil supports a small crown fringed with purple. It has a scent – oh, such a scent! Sweet and fresh, reminding me of the spring flowering trees I can just remember from my childhood. And I remember my grandfather in his garden, when I was very small. He had grass, and borders, and a vegetable patch. If something came up in his garden that he had not planted, he had a word for it: volunteer.

It is the most beautiful thing I have ever seen.

They say that there were always seeds lying in the desert sand and when it rained, they would all suddenly blossom. And it may be that there are seeds dormant around our settlement, but it has not rained since we have been here. And how long is that? We keep track of time – all the records are held in the Committee bureau, and anyone can consult them at any time. Deneb was born the year after we came so it must be about eight years.

We realised that the town was about to run dry. A clever prospecting engineer told us that he believed water could be found underground about twenty miles away. We had no idea if he was right, but it was our only hope. We left with what we could carry. Two trucks, one loaded with tools and wood and metal for the fencing, the other with every solar panel we could find. The trucks are still there, half buried in the sand on the north side of the settlement, stripped of every piece of wire and metal that could be used to make tools and needles.

On the way here we saw no-one, but there were signs that people had gone out before us. Discarded household items and clothes. At one point I remember seeing a child's watch, turquoise plastic, with a cartoon character on the dial, lying in the hot dust.

We found the Well in a low sandstone ridge in what had apparently once been an olive farm. Most of the trees were dead, but a few still held shrivelled fruit. From those we planted, we now have young trees that are beginning to produce.

When Jos comes home, he sees the dark patch in the sand around the base of the plant.

I wince at his expression.

'Please do not do this, for the children's sake if nothing else. If they cut our allowance, we will all suffer.'

I promise.

There are no materials in the depot today.

The next day he goes to work in the flax fields. I go to the weaving hall to make the fabric that goes on to the stitchers. We sometimes have green and brown dyes from the few plants we have but mostly there are only the natural colours of the fibres. We can use the variations to make stripes and by clever weaving include twills, checks and chevrons, sometimes even a jacquard effect. And when everyone has enough to wear the stitchers can make fine embroidery to decorate festival clothes.

The colours – the red-pink and purple. Is it possible the flower could give us colours again?

Galil returns for another check.

He measures it again, feels the texture of the leaves.

He stands back and looks at it.

'It is indeed a lovely thing.'

'So beautiful! Don't we need beauty?'

'Of course we do. I will do everything I can to keep it. I can't authorise water yet, but I will get one of the artists to come and draw it so that we have a record. Wait and see.'

How long do I have to wait?

It seems to grow only at night.

In the morning there are small tendrils branching out from a segment of the stem. Each has a little green node at the end. The next night is bright full moon. I sit on the stone seat outside the back door, enjoying the cool of the evening. The heat of the day still lingers in the paving and the sand. I can hear sounds of neighbours also outside in their yards. It is very peaceful.

I can hear too the sound of Jos indoors reading to the children. They have been to the papyrus exchange and have brought back a new story. Then a song and the beat of the small drum that we have on loan from the Music Centre.

In the moonlight the flower looks even more beautiful, its colours gently glowing in the calm light, the markings on its petals clear and bright. The little nodes have grown into small fruits. A pale orange colour, the skin soft and downy. I break one off and taste. It is sublime. It is so long since I have eaten anything except teff, olives and the ration of protein. It is a taste of life as it was.

I look beyond the flower, down the terraces of mud brick houses, over the flax and hemp fields and the olive trees dotted here and there, silhouetted darkly.

And to the perimeter fence and the sentry posts where the spears and axes gleam.

Beyond that the moonlight glints on the piles of white bones at the foot of the fence.

Jill Michelle
This Is What You'll Get

Keeping score? There is no point. Mother Nature always wins.
An asteroid wipes out life on Earth, and she begins again, will
Rein her species in, remind all those who choose to value
Money more than time – we can't choke her skies with toxins
And expect to breathe just fine. Reality shrinks to screens while

Politicians preen, argue the same reports both wrong and right,
Offer platitudes, small particle news to pollute the popular mind,
Lull us, huddled in our homes – lives vanished one March
    night – as
Industry's engine chugs along, swapping futures for bottom lines,
    and our
Children toss under viral dreams, tucked beneath their blankets of
Emissions; in a moment, they'll wake and ask us, *what did you
    think would happen?*

Julian Bishop
The Undertaking

They say it took an entire rainforest to create
a wooden box big enough, years to scythe
through enough seasoned ebony and teak,

an army of men accustomed to a million
innovative ways with a saw, whetted blades
slicing into the sticky gums and vital saps.

To build the box they designed incredible
airborne machines that left delicate contrails:
chalky skeletons etched on the blue sky

below them the firefly glows of a billion
lights on tarmac returned hazy signals
in reply. Day and night they hammered

beating the very oxygen into submission.
The sound drowned out frightened cries
of thrushes who abandoned their songs.

The quaggas vanished without trace.
The box took shape, globular, punctuated
by holes to release the ozone. Sad waste

materials were used to house homeless
fish. Then they banged in a battery of nails
forged in furnaces powered by oily shales.

All the people of the world came together
for once to assemble the box in a desert
stretching the length of the depleted globe –

as each plank clicked into position more light
went out until the whole Earth was encased,
then step by step they lowered it into place.

Emily Ford
Gaia Theory

The stability of life and its consistent ability to self-regulate and protect Earth's creatures connotes a universe much more intelligent than previously imagined.

Lynn Margulis and James Lovelock

They don't know about my spies
the dandelions that send their drones
the blades of grass that undulate in whispers
down my back

> *I know that by 2050, my toes and fingers will be under the sea*
> *That your five-star hotels, your promenades, your poorest relatives*
> *will be under the sea*

but you must remember,
my heart is magma. I run hot
and I don't know how I created
such cold creatures

> *I know that Yellowstone Caldera is an option for me,*
> *that you are frightened*
> *of ash up to your hips, withered crops, skies black as night from*
> *dawn to dusk and dusk to dawn*

and I will protect myself.
You best believe I will destroy
what destroys me.

Claire Booker
PROFILE SERIES 832/1: Planet E¥338-ɸ
{*in phoneme translation*}

❖ Initial analysis reveals dysfunctional atmosphere.
   Majority life-form aquatic with 6-limbed prevalence in air
   + invasive grub-like parasites (brown, pink or yellow)
   deploying water-sucking, carbon-emitting structures.

❖ Beta-scans reveal brain-wiring to be consistent with
   early Ashfruardian era.
= language, proto, with subsets.
= math-truth still embryonic: (256 bits of π at the
   two-quadrillionth (2×10^{15}th) bit).
= flesh-hubs for fuelling, repair and replication.
= internal sacks for waste.
= during reproduction, high-pitched vocalisations.
= recycling occurs around 900 moon reps (no rewind option).

❖ Rudimentary attempts already made to contact intelligent (sic)
   LIFE* (see Ashfruardian definition) beyond their solar system.

❖ Geographic swamping, resource-squander, failure to value
   LIFE* already extant on E¥338-ɸ, + self-intoxication
   with myth-concept of unique status, makes implantation
   to other planet-sectors probable.

❖ Unlikely to listen. Containment advised.

❖ Samples collected of rare anaerobic fungi and cyanobacteria.
   Also a tiny avian that uses dance code for geo-navigation.

The Things That Work
Cath Humphris

The mechanic helped me move the three potted box trees that edged the square of grass between my doorstep and the pavement. 'Are you sure?' he said, looking along the terrace, to the potted chrysanthemums and tiled paths of my neighbours. 'Why not let me take her away? I know a breaker who pays quite well for scrappers, even non-vintage models. It wouldn't be the same as crushing.'

'No need,' I said, patting Jemima's faded ermine-white flank, so elegant still, despite the miles we'd travelled. 'She should just fit here.'

Jemima's footprint was smaller than I'd realised. A narrow ribbon of lawn remained all around her.

I was happy with that; it could be tackled with the clippers left behind by the previous owners. There'd be no more puzzling over mower brochures.

Ignoring some pointed questions from my new neighbours, I kept Jemima clean and polished, but within a month she'd developed rusty rashes. Someone mentioned a petition. In the corner shop, I heard the word 'eyesore.'

Who were they to moan? I thought, as I returned home without my shopping. Petals from the winter flowering cherry tree next door were already shedding across my path. Some might call that making a mess: being inconsiderate.

But when I fetched my broom to the drift, it was flakes of ermine paint. Still, I couldn't bear to think of Jemima broken up. I swept up the evidence, as best I could.

One morning I opened the door to find the mechanic gazing at her. I made him coffee, but he wouldn't come in. 'I'm all oily,' he said. 'I wanted to tell you about a garage for rent, two roads away.'

'I couldn't afford it,' I said. I didn't add that the thought of Jemima locked in the dark hurt.

'She's only going to get worse,' he said, 'sitting out there.'

'Spring's nearly here,' I said. 'She'll be fine through the summer. It's all these storms we've been having.'

Spring that year was wetter than the winter. Muddy puddles formed along the pavements. From my rain-streaked window, I watched Jemima becoming grimy. The weather forecasters said that our clouds were carrying dust from the other side of the world.

I wanted better for my old jalopy than this slow decline, but what? The alternative was to reduce her to a cube of waste and put her on a conveyor belt, heading for a boiling vat.

It didn't feel as if the days were lengthening or warming, until I woke one Sunday, and it was summer. My neighbours were on view, washing windows and cars, tidying their front gardens, and replanting pots and urns. The street looked friendly, like the opening scene for the kind of movie I hadn't watched for a long time: like the kind of place I'd always hoped to live in.

I sat on my front doorstep, with coffee and toast, basking in the sunshine and noticed how green the street had become. The cherry tree, the little hedge that bordered my path, and the grasses, were glowing with health and vitality.

I knew then what I wanted for Jemima, it was blaze of glory, a celebration of what she'd meant.

I called up the mechanic and told him my idea. He laughed, and promised to be along shortly. Together we took out Jemima's battery, then drained the fluids from her system and he took them all away.

Then he watched as I planted honeysuckle by her exhaust pipe, cracked open the bonnet and put in three shades of cornflowers, wound down the windows so the weather could enter the interior, and sewed vegetables.

That summer, runner-beans rambled round Jemima's steering wheel, roamed over her mirrors and twined through her door handles. Radishes grew in her ashtrays and little gem lettuces cushioned her seats. A wildflower meadow sprouted on her roof. Jemima became a local celebrity, and featured in the newspaper.

When autumn storms came her wheels sank into the lawn. Puddles formed in her foot wells and diving beetles swooped in. By spring the puddles had merged. Newts scrabbled around Jemima's gear lever, and early one morning my mechanic photographed a kingfisher perched on Jemima's wing-mirror.

Words from the Brink is the third in a series of anthologies loosely linked by the theme of Maps and Mapping.
Already available:
Where We Find Ourselves, Stories and Poems of Maps and Mapping from UK Writers of the Global Majority
and *What Meets the Eye, the Deaf Perspective.*
Coming Soon:
A470, Poems for the Road/ Cerddi'r Ffordd March 2022 (Welsh and English.)

About Arachne Press

Arachne Press is a micro publisher of (award-winning!) short story and poetry anthologies and collections, novels including a Carnegie Medal nominated young adult novel, and a photographic portrait collection.

We are expanding our range all the time, but the short form is our first love. We keep fiction and poetry live, through readings, festivals (in particular our Solstice Shorts Festival), workshops, exhibitions and all things to do with writing.

https://arachnepress.com/

Follow us on Twitter:
@ArachnePress
@SolShorts

Like us on Facebook:
ArachnePress
SolsticeShorts2014

Find out more about our authors at
https://arachnepress.com/writers/